PRENTICE HALL LITERATURE

PENGUIN EDITION

Transparency Sampler

The American Experience

PEARSON

Prentice Hall

Upper Saddle River, New Jersey
Boston, Massachusetts

Transparency Sampler Contents

ISBN 0-13-250290-9

2 3 4 5 6 7 8 9 10   09 08 07 06

Graphic Organizer Transparencies

Graphic Organizer Transparencies
COMPLETE CONTENTS

UNIT 1

"The Earth on Turtle's Back" (Onondaga), **"When Grizzlies Walked Upright"** (Modoc), **from *The Navajo Origin Legend*** (Navajo), **from *The Iroquois Constitution*** (Iroquois)

Build Skills A 1
Build Skills B 2
Apply the Skills A. 3
Apply the Skills B. 4

"A Journey Through Texas" by Alvar Núñez Cabeza de Vaca

"Boulders Taller Than the Great Tower of Seville" by García López de Cárdenas

Build Skills A 5
Build Skills B 6
Apply the Skills A. 7
Apply the Skills B. 8

from *Journal of the First Voyage to America* by Christopher Columbus

Build Skills A 9
Build Skills B 10
Apply the Skills A 11
Apply the Skills B 12

from *The General History of Virginia* by John Smith

from *Of Plymouth Plantation* by William Bradford

Build Skills A 13
Build Skills B 14
Apply the Skills A 15
Apply the Skills B 16

"Huswifery" by Edward Taylor

"To My Dear and Loving Husband" by Anne Bradstreet

Build Skills A 17
Build Skills B 18
Apply the Skills A. 19
Apply the Skills B. 20

from *Sinners in the Hands of an Angry God* by Jonathan Edwards

Build Skills A 21
Build Skills B 22
Apply the Skills A. 23
Apply the Skills B. 24

Writing Workshop: Rubric for Self-Assessment 25

Unit 2

from *The Autobiography* and **from *Poor Richard's Almanack*** by Benjamin Franklin

Build Skills A 26
Build Skills B 27
Apply the Skills A. 28
Apply the Skills B. 29

from *The Interesting Narrative of the Life of Olaudah Equiano* by Olaudah Equiano

Build Skills A 30
Build Skills B 31
Apply the Skills A. 32
Apply the Skills B. 33

The Declaration of Independence by Thomas Jefferson

from *The Crisis, Number 1,* by Thomas Paine

Build Skills A 34
Build Skills B 35
Apply the Skills A. 36
Apply the Skills B. 37

"An Hymn to the Evening" and **"To His Excellency, General Washington"** by Phillis Wheatley

Build Skills A 38
Build Skills B 39
Apply the Skills A. 40
Apply the Skills B. 41

"Speech in the Virginia Convention"
by Patrick Henry

"Speech in the Convention"
by Benjamin Franklin
Build Skills A 42
Build Skills B 43
Apply the Skills A. 44
Apply the Skills B. 45

"Letter to Her Daughter from the New White House" by Abigail Adams

from *Letters from an American Farmer*
by Michel-Guillaume Jean de Crèvecoeur
Build Skills A 46
Build Skills B 47
Apply the Skills A. 48
Apply the Skills B. 49

Writing Workshop: Rubric for
Self-Assessment 50

UNIT 3

"The Devil and Tom Walker"
by Washington Irving
Build Skills A 51
Build Skills B 52
Apply the Skills A. 53
Apply the Skills B. 54

"The Tide Rises, The Tide Falls"
by Henry Wadsworth Longfellow

"Thanatopsis" by William Cullen Bryant

"Old Ironsides" by Oliver Wendell Holmes

from *Snowbound*
by John Greenleaf Whittier
Build Skills A 55
Build Skills B 56
Apply the Skills A. 57
Apply the Skills B. 58

"Crossing the Great Divide"
by Meriwether Lewis

"The Most Sublime Spectacle on Earth" by John Wesley Powell
Build Skills A 59
Build Skills B 60
Apply the Skills A. 61
Apply the Skills B. 62

"The Fall of the House of Usher" and **"The Raven"** by Edgar Allan Poe
Build Skills A 63
Build Skills B 64
Apply the Skills A. 65
Apply the Skills B. 66

"The Minister's Black Veil"
by Nathaniel Hawthorne
Build Skills A 67
Build Skills B 68
Apply the Skills A. 68
Apply the Skills B. 70

from *Moby-Dick* by Herman Melville
Build Skills A 71
Build Skills B 72
Apply the Skills A. 73
Apply the Skills B. 74

from *Nature,* **from** *Self-Reliance,* **"The Snowstorm,** and **"Concord Hymn"**
by Ralph Waldo Emerson
Build Skills A 75
Build Skills B 76
Apply the Skills A. 77
Apply the Skills B. 78

from *Walden* **and from** *Civil Disobedience* by Henry David Thoreau
Build Skills A 79
Build Skills B 80
Apply the Skills A. 81
Apply the Skills B. 82

Emily Dickinson's Poetry
Build Skills A 83
Build Skills B 84
Apply the Skills A. 85
Apply the Skills B. 86

Walt Whitman's Poetry

    Build Skills A 87

    Build Skills B 88

    Apply the Skills A. 89

    Apply the Skills B. 90

Writing Workshop: Rubric for

    Self-Assessment 91

UNIT 4

"An Episode of War" by Stephen Crane

"Willie Has Gone to the War"

by George Cooper and Stephen Foster

    Build Skills A 92

    Build Skills B 93

    Apply the Skills A. 94

    Apply the Skills B. 95

"Swing Low, Sweet Chariot"

"Go Down, Moses"

    Build Skills A 96

    Build Skills B 97

    Apply the Skills A. 98

    Apply the Skills B. 99

from *My Bondage and My Freedom*

by Frederick Douglass

    Build Skills A 100

    Build Skills B 101

    Apply the Skills A. 102

    Apply the Skills B. 103

"An Occurrence at Owl Creek Bridge"

by Ambrose Bierce

    Build Skills A 104

    Build Skills B 105

    Apply the Skills A. 106

    Apply the Skills B. 107

"The Gettysburg Address" and
"Second Inaugural Address"

by Abraham Lincoln

    Build Skills A 108

    Build Skills B 109

    Apply the Skills A. 110

    Apply the Skills B. 111

from Civil War Diaries, Journals, and Letters

    Build Skills A 112

    Build Skills B 113

    Apply the Skills A. 114

    Apply the Skills B. 115

"The Boy's Ambition" from *Life on the Mississippi* and **"The Notorious Jumping Frog of Calaveras County"** by Mark Twain

    Build Skills A 116

    Build Skills B 117

    Apply the Skills A. 118

    Apply the Skills B. 119

"The Outcasts of Poker Flat"

by Bret Harte

    Build Skills A 120

    Build Skills B 121

    Apply the Skills A. 122

    Apply the Skills B. 123

"Heading West" by Miriam Davis Colt

"I Will Fight No More Forever"

by Chief Joseph

    Build Skills A 124

    Build Skills B 125

    Apply the Skills A. 126

    Apply the Skills B. 127

"To Build a Fire" by Jack London

    Build Skills A 128

    Build Skills B 129

    Apply the Skills A. 130

    Apply the Skills B. 131

"The Story of an Hour" by Kate Chopin

    Build Skills A 132

    Build Skills B 133

    Apply the Skills A. 134

    Apply the Skills B. 135

"Douglass" and **"We Wear the Mask"**

by Paul Laurence Dunbar

    Build Skills A 136

    Build Skills B 137

    Apply the Skills A. 138

    Apply the Skills B. 139

"Luke Havergal" and "Richard Cory" by Edwin Arlington Robinson

"Lucinda Matlock" and "Richard Bone" by Edgar Lee Masters

Build Skills A 140
Build Skills B 141
Apply the Skills A. 142
Apply the Skills B. 143

"A Wagner Matinee" by Willa Cather

Build Skills A 144
Build Skills B 145
Apply the Skills A. 146
Apply the Skills B. 147

Writing Workshop: Rubric for Self-Assessment 148

UNIT 5

"The Love Song of J. Alfred Prufrock" by T. S. Eliot

Build Skills A 149
Build Skills B 150
Apply the Skills A. 151
Apply the Skills B. 152

Imagist Poets

Build Skills A 153
Build Skills B 154
Apply the Skills A. 155
Apply the Skills B. 156

"Winter Dreams" by F. Scott Fitzgerald

Build Skills A 157
Build Skills B 158
Apply the Skills A. 159
Apply the Skills B. 160

"The Turtle" from *The Grapes of Wrath* by John Steinbeck

Build Skills A 161
Build Skills B 162
Apply the Skills A. 163
Apply the Skills B. 164

"old age sticks" and **"anyone lived in a pretty how town"** by E. E. Cummings

"The Unknown Citizen" by W. H. Auden

Build Skills A 165
Build Skills B 166
Apply the Skills A. 167
Apply the Skills B. 168

"The Far and the Near" by Thomas Wolfe

Build Skills A 169
Build Skills B 170
Apply the Skills A. 171
Apply the Skills B. 172

"Of Modern Poetry" and "Anecdote of the Jar" by Wallace Stevens

"Ars Poetica" by Archibald MacLeish

"Poetry" by Marianne Moore

Build Skills A 173
Build Skills B 174
Apply the Skills A. 175
Apply the Skills B. 176

"In Another Country" by Ernest Hemingway

"The Corn Planting" by Sherwood Anderson

"A Worn Path" by Eudora Welty

Build Skills A 177
Build Skills B 178
Apply the Skills A. 179
Apply the Skills B. 180

"Chicago" and "Grass" by Carl Sandburg

Build Skills A 181
Build Skills B 182
Apply the Skills A. 183
Apply the Skills B. 184

"The Jilting of Granny Weatherall" by Katherine Anne Porter

Build Skills A 185
Build Skills B 186
Apply the Skills A. 187
Apply the Skills B. 188

A Rose for Emily" and "Nobel Prize Acceptance Speech"
by William Faulkner
Build Skills A 189
Build Skills B 190
Apply the Skills A 191
Apply the Skills B 192

Robert Frost's Poetry
Build Skills A 193
Build Skills B 194
Apply the Skills A 195
Apply the Skills B 196

"The Night the Ghost Got In"
by James Thurber

from Here Is New York by E. B. White
Build Skills A 197
Build Skills B 198
Apply the Skills A 199
Apply the Skills B 200

from Dust Tracks on a Road
by Zora Neale Hurston
Build Skills A 201
Build Skills B 202
Apply the Skills A 203
Apply the Skills B 204

**"The Negro Speaks of Rivers,"
"Ardella," "Dream Variations,"** and
"Refugee in America"
by Langston Hughes

"The Tropics in New York"
by Claude McKay
Build Skills A 205
Build Skills B 206
Apply the Skills A 207
Apply the Skills B 208

"From the Dark Tower"
by Countee Cullen

"A Black Man Talks of Reaping"
by Arna Bontemps

"Storm Ending" by Jean Toomer
Build Skills A 209
Build Skills B 210
Apply the Skills A 211
Apply the Skills B 212

Writing Workshop: Rubric for
Self-Assessment 213

UNIT 6

"The Life You Save May Be Your Own"
by Flannery O'Connor
Build Skills A 214
Build Skills B 215
Apply the Skills A 216
Apply the Skills B 217

"The First Seven Years"
by Bernard Malamud
Build Skills A 218
Build Skills B 219
Apply the Skills A 220
Apply the Skills B 221

"The Writer in the Family"
by E. L. Doctorow
Build Skills A 222
Build Skills B 223
Apply the Skills A 224
Apply the Skills B 225

"Aliceville" by Tony Earley
Build Skills A 226
Build Skills B 227
Apply the Skills A 228
Apply the Skills B 229

"Gold Glade" by Robert Penn Warren

"The Light Comes Brighter"
by Theodore Roethke

"Traveling Through the Dark"
by William Stafford
Build Skills A 230
Build Skills B 231
Apply the Skills A 232
Apply the Skills B 233

"Average Waves in Unprotected Waters" by Anne Tyler

    Build Skills A 234

    Build Skills B 235

    Apply the Skills A. 236

    Apply the Skills B. 237

From *The Names* by N. Scott Momaday

"Mint Snowball" by Naomi Shihab Nye

"Suspended" by Joy Harjo

    Build Skills A 238

    Build Skills B 239

    Apply the Skills A. 240

    Apply the Skills B. 241

"Everyday Use" by Alice Walker

    Build Skills A 242

    Build Skills B 243

    Apply the Skills A. 244

    Apply the Skills B. 245

from *The Woman Warrior*

    by Maxine Hong Kingston

    Build Skills A 246

    Build Skills B 247

    Apply the Skills A. 248

    Apply the Skills B. 249

"Antojos" by Julia Alvarez

    Build Skills A 250

    Build Skills B 251

    Apply the Skills A. 252

    Apply the Skills B. 253

"Who Burns for the Perfection of Paper" by Martin Espada

"Most Satisfied by Snow" by Diana Chang

"Hunger in New York City" by Simon Ortiz

"What For" by Garret Hongo

    Build Skills A 254

    Build Skills B 255

    Apply the Skills A. 256

    Apply the Skills B. 257

"Onomatopoeia" by William Safire

"Coyote v. Acme" by Ian Frazier

"Loneliness…An American Malady" by Carson McCullers

"One Day, Broken in Two" By Anna Quindlen

    Build Skills A 258

    Build Skills B 259

    Apply the Skills A. 260

    Apply the Skills B. 261

"Straw Into Gold" by Sandra Cisneros

"For the Love of Books" by Rita Dove

"Mother Tongue" by Amy Tan

    Build Skills A 262

    Build Skills B 263

    Apply the Skills A. 264

    Apply the Skills B. 265

"The Rockpile" by James Baldwin

    Build Skills A 266

    Build Skills B 267

    Apply the Skills A. 268

    Apply the Skills B. 269

from *Hiroshima* by John Hersey

"Losses" and **"The Death of the Ball Turret Gunner"** by Randall Jarrell

    Build Skills A 270

    Build Skills B 271

    Apply the Skills A. 272

    Apply the Skills B. 273

"Mirror" by Sylvia Plath

"In a Classroom" by Adrienne Rich

"The Explorer" by Gwendolyn Brooks

"Frederick Douglass" and **"Runagate Runagate"** by Robert Hayden

    Build Skills A 274

    Build Skills B 275

    Apply the Skills A. 276

    Apply the Skills B. 277

Inaugural Address by John F. Kennedy

from *Letter from Birmingham City Jail* by Dr. Martin Luther King, Jr.

    Build Skills A 278

    Build Skills B 279

    Apply the Skills A. 280

    Apply the Skills B. 281

"For My Children" by Colleen McElroy

"Bidwell Ghost" by Louise Erdrich

"Camouflaging the Chimera" by Yusef Komunyakaa

    Build Skills A 282

    Build Skills B 283

    Apply the Skills A. 284

    Apply the Skills B. 285

***The Crucible*, Act I** by Arthur Miller

    Build Skills A 286

    Build Skills B 287

    Apply the Skills A. 288

    Apply the Skills B. 289

***The Crucible*, Act II** by Arthur Miller

    Build Skills A 290

    Build Skills B 291

    Apply the Skills A. 292

    Apply the Skills B. 293

***The Crucible*, Act III** by Arthur Miller

    Build Skills A 294

    Build Skills B 295

    Apply the Skills A. 296

    Apply the Skills B. 297

***The Crucible*, Act IV** by Arthur Miller

    Build Skills A 298

    Build Skills B 299

    Apply the Skills A. 300

    Apply the Skills B. 301

Writing Workshop: Rubric for Self-Assessment 302

GENERIC ORGANIZERS

Analyze Conclude Diagram. 241

Author's Purpose Chart 242

Cause-and-Effect Flowchart 243

Character Wheel 244

Cluster Diagram 245

Five-Column Chart 246

Outline. 247

Plot Diagram. 248

Series-of-Events Chain 249

Three-column Chart 250

Three-way Venn Diagram. 251

Timeline 252

Two-column Chart. 253

Venn Diagram. 254

Web 255

Word Map. 256

Blank Transparency 257